Originally published in 2018 by Christell A Chapin, Freestone Publishings, Inc, Post Falls ID 83854. Library of Congress catalog in publication data.

The Gingerbread House / c by Christell A Chapin: (artwork by Christell A Chapin).

Summary: Leroy and Libby are two little mice who find themselves homeless and hungry due to a horrible winter storm. Join these adorable mice in this sweet little tale as they learn lessons about sharing, the power of prayer and gratitude and lastly, they discover each other's company is by far more valuable than anything they could ever own.

(1. Juvenile Fiction – Mice, 2. Juvenile Fiction – Poetry)

I. Chapin, Christell, ill. II. Title.

ISBN: 978-1-953108-01-2

Written & Illustrated By

Christell A Chapin

The Gingerbread House

Leroy and Libby had a box for a house,
But it wasn't a very good house for a mouse.
It had no windows, just one big door,
With a cardboard ceiling, walls and floor.

There were no tables or chairs,
Or sofas or beds,
Just a dry little corner
To lay both their heads.

There was just enough room
For a family of two,
And Leroy and Libby
Made that little house do.

Until one cold, snowy, winter's day,
When the snow on the roof,
Made the roof fall away.

"Don't worry, Libby." said Leroy,
"We'll find another one soon.
A great big house with windows,
And plenty of extra room.

A house far better,
Than you've ever seen,
I promise you, Libby,
The house of your dreams!"

"I'm not worried, Leroy,
Any house will do.
Makes no difference where I live,
As long as I'm with you."

"I made these things for Christmas,
But since the day is almost here,
And the weather keeps getting colder,
We may need them now, I fear."

"Merry Christmas, Leroy!" she said,
As she grabbed a wrapped gift by a tree.
"Oh, my goodness, Libby!" he cried,
"This coat is just perfect for me!"

They came across an old soup can
Laying in the snow,
But it just rolled from side to side
And so, they had to go.

"Oh no dear, Libby," said Leroy,
"This house will never do!
I won't stop until I find
The perfect house for you."

"A pretty house doesn't matter," she said,
"If you look at it on its own.
It's the love that fills the walls inside,
That makes a house a home."

Though Libby kept trying to tell him,
Happiness couldn't be bought,
Leroy just didn't understand,
"Her house must be perfect!" he thought.

The next day, by a restaurant,
Down an alley, near the back,
Set a row of lovely boxes…
But the neighbor was a cat.

They searched for days,
But could not find,
A house to keep them warm.
Now things were getting dangerous,
Because of the winter storm.

"We need food and shelter," said Leroy,
"And we need it right away!
If we don't get some help real soon…"

"Please, Leroy!...
Let's just pray!"

Just then Leroy happened to see,
A church's outdoor nativity.

"I've got to get you
Somewhere warm,
Away from this snow,
My dear."

"Why, this manger will be perfect.
Now, you just wait right here."

"I want to help you look for shelter."
Libby shivered as she cried.
"Please wait under this manger, dear,
I know how hard you've tried."

"But your little hands are freezing, Libby,
And so are your tiny feet!
I've got to find a place for us…
Maybe down this very street."

Leroy bounced out down the road
As fast as he could go,
And as he went, she heard him yell,
"I'll be back before you know!"

The snow just kept on falling
Covering everything in sight
With its icy winter blanket
Of frozen snowflake white.

Libby closed her ice, cold eyes,
And said a little prayer,
"Thank you, God," she whispered,
"For the years of loving care.

I guess you're awful busy,
And I'm sure you have a plan,

But if you would,
We certainly could,

Use a helping hand."

After all his searching for
A "PERFECT" house,
Leroy realized he'd been wrong.

Just being together
Was what mattered most,
Libby was right all along.

Leroy was getting worried,
Tomorrow would be Christmas Day.

"Lord, please help us, if you would,
Find a place to stay!"

It seemed very unlikely
That any food could be found
But there, to his amazement
Was a cookie on the ground!

As he was rushing back to Libby,
To share this special treat,
He saw a hungry family of squirrels,
Searching for something to eat.

"Merry Christmas." said Leroy,
As he broke the cookie in two.
Before the family scampered off,
They thanked him and cried,
"God bless you!"

"My darling, Libby, is freezing Lord!
Whatever shall I do?
Please help me find a home for her…
ANY place will do!"

Just then a big door swung open
And out stepped a jolly old man.
"This is for you, little fellow!" he said,
And he had a small key in his hand.

The BEST BAKERY

GINGERBREAD
House
Sale $9.⁹⁹

Leroy was so thankful
That he began to cry.
There, before him
Was a house so grand,
He could hardly believe his eyes!

There were tables and chairs,
And a warm little bed,
And it was all made out of
GINGERBREAD!

It had lots of windows
And a door the right size,
"I can't wait to get, Libby!
She'll be so surprised!"

"Look how God has blessed us, Libby!
It's perfect in every way!"

"Oh, my goodness, Leroy!" she gasped,
"I don't know what to say!"

As Libby cried tears of joy,
She smiled and said with a kiss,

"In all my dreams,
I've never seen
A more beautiful home
Than this!"

"It couldn't be any more perfect," he said,
"Without a doubt that's true.
But the blessing that I love most of all is,
I get to share it with you!"

Leroy and Libby thanked God up above,
For answering their prayers,
With such kindness and love.

Dinner was ready and the table was set.
It would be a Christmas,
They'd never forget.

And from that day forward,
I heard it was said,
To all who were hungry,
They fed gingerbread.

God Bless
Our Home

The End

To make your own
Christmas treat,
See Libby's recipe,
It's super sweet.
It's extra easy
And especially fun,
Your baking tradition,
Has now begun!

Gingerbread Cookie Recipe

Cream Together:
2/3 Cup Butter
1/2 Cup Brown Sugar

Add, Then Mix Well:
1/2 Cup Molasses
1 teaspoon Vanilla
1 Egg

Combine Together, Then Gradually Add to Cream Mixture & Mix Well:
3 Cups All-Purpose Flour
1 teaspoon Baking Soda
1 teaspoon of Each:
Cinnamon, Ginger and Allspice
1/2 teaspoon Salt
1/2 teaspoon Ground Nutmeg

Icing:
1 1/2 Cup Powdered Sugar
4 teaspoons Milk & 1 teaspoon Lemon Juice
1 Tablespoon Melted Butter

DRECTIONS

Cream together butter and sugar. Add molasses, vanilla and egg; mix well. In a separate bowl, combine the flour, baking soda, cinnamon, ginger, allspice, salt and nutmeg; then gradually add to creamed mixture and mix well.

Divide dough in half. Refrigerate for at least 2 hours.

On a lightly floured surface, roll out each portion of dough to 1/8" thickness. Cut with cookie cutter dipped in flour. Place 2 in. apart on greased baking sheets.

Bake at 350° for 9-11 minutes or until edges are firm. Remove to wire racks to cool. Decorate as desired. Makes 2 dozen medium size cookies.

"I was hungry, and you fed me; I was thirsty, and you gave me something to drink."
Matthew 25:35

"When you did this for anyone of mine, then you did this for me."
Matthew 25:40

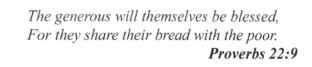

The generous will themselves be blessed,
For they share their bread with the poor.
Proverbs 22:9

No act of kindness, no matter how small,
Is ever wasted.

- Aesop -

CPSIA information can be obtained
at www.ICGtesting.com
Printed in the USA
LVHW071529051222
734608LV00002B/32